Pob's Poems and Word Games

Pob read a poem
and it made him laugh.
A poem to Teddy he read.
This is a good one,
listen to this.
But Ted was asleep
in his bed.

Pob's Poems and Word Games

Chosen by
Anne Wood and Robin Stevens

Researched by Sara Conkey

Illustrated by Malcolm Bird

A Magnet Book

First published in 1988 as a Magnet paperback original
by Methuen Children's Books Ltd
11 New Fetter Lane, London EC4P 4EE
This collection copyright © 1988 Anne Wood and Robin Stevens
Illustrations copyright © 1988 Malcolm Bird
Printed in Great Britain
by Cox & Wyman Ltd, Reading

ISBN 0-416-08632-2

Contents

The Little Maid	Anon	7
Beneath the Stairs	Sara Conkey	8
The Seaside	Paul Oakley	10
At the Seaside	Robert Louis Stevenson	11
Two of Them	Anon	12
The Pedlar's Caravan	William Brightly Rands	13
A Rhyme for Little Folks	Kate M. Cleary	14
The Conker Tree	J. Tuckley	16
Pob's Puzzles		17
A Tragic Story	William Makepeace Thackery	26
Spring into Summer	Karen Auckland	28
Queen Nephatiti	Anon	29
I Could . . .	Sara Conkey	30
One, Two, Three	Traditional	31
My Shadow	Robert Louis Stevenson	32
The Fan	Shammi Choudbury	34
Baby	Christina Rossetti	35
Anna Elise	Anon	36
Indoors	adapted by Sara Conkey	37
When Mamma was a Little Girl	Grace F. Coolidge	38
Pob's Riddles		40
Blue Things	Christopher Morgan	42
The Vowels	Jonathan Swift	43
The Three Little Pigs	Alfred Scott Gatty	44
A Fish in the Sea	John Chalmers	46
Birds on a Stone	Anon	47
I Had a Little Crocodile	Sara Conkey	48
Horatio Hamilton Harries	Anon	50
Fishy Tale	Christina Rossetti	51
Bed in Summer	Robert Louis Stevenson	52
Me and My Dog	Anna Drodge	53
The Skipping-Rope	Mrs Charles Heaton	54
Go to Bed	Anon	55
Water	Andrew Thorne	56
The Sad Story of a Little Boy That Cried	Anon	57

How the Little Kite Learnt to Fly	Anon	58
The Sea	Fiona Sharples	60
An Alphabet of Children	Isabel Frances Bellows	61
Pob's Alphabet		69
Early and Late	W. S. Reed	73
A Song of Myself	John Keats	74
My Three Cows	Sam Clarke	76
A.B.C.	Anon	77
What Became of Them?	Anon	78
Mr Blackbird	Lynn Maloney	80
Mrs Mason	Anon	81
Long Time Ago	Anon	82
Pob Says, 'Take Note!'		84
Poor Starving Children	Michael Algate	91
Choosing Their Names	Thomas Hood	92
Three Wise Men of Gotham	Traditional	94

The Little Maid

There was a little maid
Who wore a great big bonnet,
And she had a little frock
With a great big bow upon it.
She took a little walk
Along the great big road,
And on a little stone
She saw a great big toad.
It gave one little croak
And took a great big leap,
Which made the little maid
Give just one great big squeak.

Anon

Beneath the Stairs

Beneath the stairs I like to creep
It's nice, and quiet, and no one peeps
It's dark and I can say my prayers
When I sit beneath the stairs

Sometimes beneath the stairs at dusk
I go to India on an elephant's tusk
I fly into forests, make friends with bears
I do all this beneath the stairs

Beneath the stairs I'm on the moon
I'm crossing the sun in a yellow balloon
I have tea with tigers and in lions' lairs
What adventures there are beneath the stairs!

I walk across strange and ancient lands
I walk through snow and over sands
And never have I the slightest cares
I'm brave, when I'm beneath the stairs

Beneath the stairs I like to rest
It is the place that I like best
For I can travel anywhere!
When I sit beneath the stairs

Sara Conkey

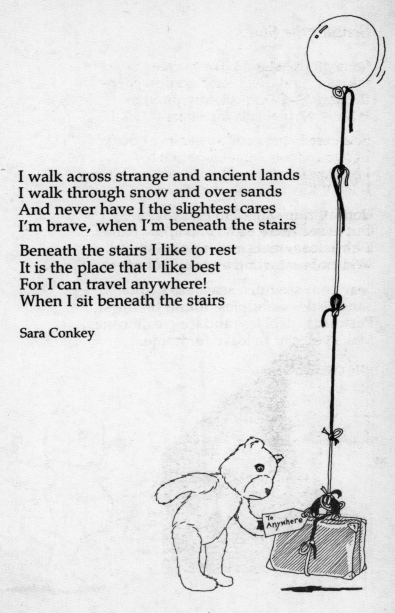

The Seaside

Donkey rides and fish and chips,
Out at sea there's lots of ships,
Lighthouse, piers and seaside shows,
And crabs crawl up and nip your toes.

Seaweed, seagulls, seashells galore,
Sandcastles, sandpies, found on the shore,
Postcards, pebbles, and ice cream cones,
Make you sad to leave for home.

Paul Oakley
Age 5

At the Seaside

When I was down beside the sea
A wooden spade they gave to me
To dig beside the sandy shore
My holes were empty like a cup
In every hole the sea came up
Til it could come no more.

Robert Louis Stevenson

Two of Them

Grandfather's come to see baby today,
Dear little, queer little baby Ned;
With his toothless mouth, his double chin,
And never a hair on his shiny head,
He looks in the pretty eyes of blue,
Where the baby's soul is peeping through,
And cries, with many a loving kiss,
'Hallo! what little old man is this?'

Baby stares in grandfather face,
Merry old, cheery old 'Grandfather Ned',
With his toothless mouth, his double chin,
And never a hair on his dear old head;
He scans him solemnly up and down,
From his double chin to his smooth, bald crown,
And says to himself as babies do,
'Hallo! can this be a baby, too?'

Anon

The Pedlar's Caravan

I wish I lived in a caravan
With a horse to drive, like the pedlar-man!
Where he comes from nobody knows,
Or where he goes to, but on he goes!

His caravan has windows two,
And a chimney of tin, that the smoke comes
    through;
He has a wife with a baby brown,
And they go riding from town to town.

Chairs to mend, and delft to sell!
He clashes the basins like a bell;
Tea-trays, baskets ranged in order,
Plates with the alphabet round the border!

The roads are brown, and the sea is green,
But his house is just like a bathing-machine;
The world is round, but he can ride,
Rumble and splash, to the other side!

William Brightly Rands

A Rhyme for Little Folks

Oh, I'll tell you a story that nobody knows,
Of ten little fingers and ten little toes,
Of two pretty eyes and one little nose,
   And where they all went one day.

Oh, the little round nose smelled something sweet,
So sweet it must surely be nice to eat,
And patter away went two little feet
   Out of the room one day.

Ten little toes climbed up on a chair.
Two eyes peeped over a big shelf where
Lay a lovely cake, all frosted and fair,
   Made by Mamma that day.

The mouth grew round and the eyes grew big
At taste of the sugar, the spice, the fig;
And ten little fingers went dig, dig, dig,
   Into the cake that day.

And when Mamma kissed a curly head,
Cuddling it cosily up in bed;
'I wonder, was there a mouse,' she said,
   'Out on the shelf today?'

'Oh, Mamma, yes,' and a laugh of glee
Like fairy bells rang merrily –
'But the little bit of a mouse was *me*,
   Out on the shelf today!'

Kate M Cleary

The Conker Tree

The conker tree is golden yellow
like the sun,
It shakes in the crisp morning air,
It towers over you like a giant
sleeping
And when the wind roars it awakes

J Tuckley
Age 11

Pob's Puzzles

Can you think of the missing words?
Pob's left a picture clue

1
Round and round the flowers
there flies a
He's collecting nectar
to make   for my tea.

2
The   had lost his ring,
and the Queen had lost her
Together they searched high and low,
all around the town.

17

3

When the moon is in the sky
and ☆☆☆☆ are overhead,
I know it's time to say good night
and go upstairs to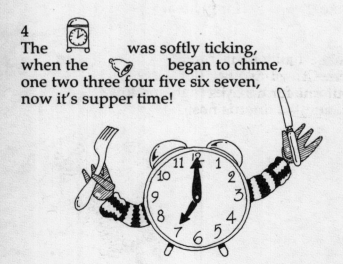

4

The 🕐 was softly ticking,
when the 🔔 began to chime,
one two three four five six seven,
now it's supper time!

18

5
When you're in the
you can see a big snake squirm,
but when you're in the garden
you can only see a

6
I can make a jolly man
everytime it
with buttons for his eyes
and a   for his nose.

7
Pack a and buy a ticket
with a five pound note,
then sail with me across the sea
aboard my sturdy

8
When I've eaten
I go to bed and dream,
that I ate something nicer,
such as and cream.

Humm^{m m m m}_{m m} m m m m m m m m

9
John can play the violin,
Jill can play the 🥁
Josey can't play anything
so all he does is hummmm

10
Doing up my 👟 laces
is very hard indeed.
I'm glad I've only got two feet
unlike a 🐛

z z z z z z z z z z z z z z

11
The  he was counting sheep
to check that he had 🐑🐑🐑🐑🐑🐑🐑🐑🐑🐑
But half-way through he fell asleep
and had to start again.

12
are a yellow colour
so are lemons too.
Apples can be red or green,
but never ever Blue

13
Normal cats can catch a
normal cats climb trees.
But lazy cats won't climb the stairs
and all they catch are

14
Mandy is a china
she doesn't laugh or cry
but when I'm good I'm sure I see
a   in her eye.

15
An ![elephant] is very big
and very very strong
but most of all his ![trunk] is
very very VERY long.

16
Wipe the ![window] , wash the floor,
beat the carpet clean,
then no one else will ever know
where the ![mess] has been.

24

17
I make a great loud stamping noise
when my are on,
but if I tiptoe in my
you won't know where I've gone!

18
Granny has a ▬▬▬▬▬ coat
she often lets me try on.
I get down on my hands and knees
and pretend I'm a

A Tragic Story

There lived a sage in days of yore,
And he a handsome pigtail wore;
But wondered much and sorrowed more,
Because it hung behind him.

He mused upon this curious case,
And swore he'd change the pigtail's place
And have it hanging at his face,
Not dangling there behind him.

Says he, 'The Mystery I've found, –
I'll turn me round,'
He turned him round;
But still it hung behind him.

A sage is a clever person – are you clever?

Then round and round, and out and in,
All day the puzzled sage did spin;
In vain – it mattered not a pin –
The pigtail hung behind him.

And right, and left, and round about,
And up and down, and in, and out
He turned; but still the pigtail stout
Hung steadily behind him.

And though his efforts never slack,
And though he twist, and twirl, and tack,
Alas! still faithful to his back,
The pigtail hangs behind him.

William Makepeace Thackery

Spring Into Summer

Spring into summer
The sun shining high
Daisies are blowing
In a soft breezy sky
Soft grass is growing
Moss sprouting up
Soon they'll be growing small buttercups.

Birds singing softly
Ladybirds crawl
Goldfish are lying in the cool school pool
Green leaves are blowing
Butterflies flit
Fluttering softly in a deep blue sky.

Karen Auckland
Age 10

Queen Nephatiti

Spin-a-coin, spin-a-coin, all fall down
Queen Nephatiti stalks through the town.
Over the pavements her feet go clack
Her legs are as tall as a chimney stack.
Her fingers flicker like snakes in the air
Walls split open at her green-eyed stare.
Her voice is as thin as the ghosts of bees
She will crumble your bones, she will make your
    blood freeze.
Spin-a-coin, spin-a-coin, all fall down
Queen Nephatiti stalks through the town.

Anon

I Could. . .

I could capture the moon

In a net
And I bet I could unplug the sea
Without getting wet.
I could catch the wind
In my hat
and fly to the stars
On a cricket bat.
I could number the raindrops
and know every one
I could carry a mountain
I could juggle the sun
I could sprinkle the desert
From a pepperpot
I could walk through a furnace
Without getting hot.

If I could do all this
I suppose
I could do
Quite a lot.

Sara Conkey

One, Two, Three

One, two, three
Mother caught a flea
She put it in a tea-pot
And made a cup of tea
The flea jumped out
Mother gave a shout
And in came father
With his shirt hanging out.

Traditional

My Shadow

I have a little shadow that goes in and out with me
And what can be the use of him is more than I can
   see.
He is very, very like me from the heels up to the
   head,
And I see him jump before me, when I jump into
   my bed.

The funniest thing about him is the way he likes to
   grow –
Not at all like proper children, which is always very
   slow,
For he sometimes shoots up taller like an india-
   rubber ball,
And he sometimes gets so little that there's none of
   him at all.

He hasn't got a notion of how children ought to
   play,
And can only make a fool of me in every sort of
   way.
He stays so close beside me; he's a coward you can
   see,
I'd think shame to stick to nursie as that shadow
   sticks to me!

One morning, very early, before the sun was up,
I rose and found the shining dew on every
   buttercup;
but my lazy little shadow, like an arrant sleepy
   head,
Had stayed at home behind me and was fast asleep
   in bed.

Robert Louis Stevenson

The Fan

There was a young lady called Ann,
Who was given a beautiful fan,
She held it in place,
To cover her face,
And attracted a handsome man.
He called on her one day for tea,
Dressed up in his best finer-ee
He said, 'My sweet dove,
It is you that I love,
Will you please please marry me?'
She smiled and played with the fan,
And then into his arms she ran.
He held her so tight,
She fainted in fright,
What a sad end for Ann.

Shammi Choudbury

Baby

My baby has a mottled fist,
My baby has a neck in creases;
My baby kisses and is kissed,
For he's the very thing for kisses.

Christina Rossetti

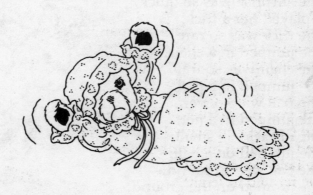

Anna Elise

Anna Elise
She jumped with surprise;
The surprise was so quick,
It played her a trick;
The trick was so rare,
She jumped in a chair;
The chair was so frail,
She jumped in a pail;
The pail was so wet,
She jumped in a net;
The net was so small,
She jumped on a ball;
The ball was so round,
She jumped on the ground;
And ever since then
   she's been turning around.

Anon

36

Indoors

It rains on the flowers
It rains on the sea
It rains on a Sunday
But not on me!

It snows on a mountain
It snows on a tree
It always snows on holidays
But not on me!

The sun shines on playgrounds
The sun shines on bees
The sun is shining outside
But never on me!

Adapted from an old rhyme by Sara Conkey

When Mamma was a Little Girl

When Mamma was a little girl
   (Or so they say to me),
She never used to romp and run,
Nor shout and scream with noisy fun,
   Nor climb an apple-tree.
She always kept her hair in curl, –
When Mamma was a little girl.

When Mamma was a little girl
　(It seems to her, you see),
She never used to tumble down,
Nor break her doll, nor tear her gown,
　Nor drink her papa's tea.
She learned to knit, 'plain', 'seam', and 'purl',
When Mamma was a little girl.

But grandma says, – it must be true, –
'How fast the seasons o'er us whirl!
Your Mamma, dear, was just like you,
　When she was grandma's little girl!'

Grace F Coolidge

39

Pob's Riddles

Thirty white horses
Upon a red hill
Now they tramp
Now they champ
Now they stand still.

(tongue and teeth)

I live on a very narrow space
And I have a round white face
Twice daily my hands say the same thing
Yet every time fresh news I bring.

(clock)

A diamond shape in the sky
I have no face, I have no eye
But a tail I do possess
Just how long you'll have to guess
In the clouds, birds pass me by
But without any wings I can fly!

(kite)

My body is thin
I've nothing within
I'm silver from my top to my toe
I have no feet
But I make things neat
And I help everyone to sew.

(pin)

Blue Things

The blue sky that is up above us
The blue sails on the blue sea
And the bluebells swaying in the wind
Are all the things I love to see.

Blue cars whizzing in and out
The blue ink flowing from pens
Blue shirts blowing on the line
And blue birds through the camera lens.

Christopher Morgan
Age 11

The Vowels

We are very little creatures
All of different voice and features
One of us in glAss is set
One of us you'll find in jEt
T'other you may see in tIn
And the fourth a bOx within
If the fifth you would pursue
It can never fly from yoU.

Jonathan Swift

The Three Little Pigs

A jolly old sow once lived in a sty,
  And three little piggies had she,
And she waddled about saying 'Umph! umph!
  umph!'
  While the little ones said 'Wee! wee!'

'My dear little brothers,' said one of the brats,
  'My dear little piggies,' said he;
'Let us all for the future say Umph! umph! umph!
  'Tis so childish to say Wee! wee!,'

Then these little pigs grew skinny and lean,
  And lean they might very well be;
For somehow they *couldn't* say 'Umph! umph!
  umph!'
  And they *wouldn't* say 'Wee! wee! wee!'

UMPH   UMPH

So after a time these little pigs died,
  They all died as quick as can be
From trying too hard to say 'Umph! umph! umph!'
  When they only could say 'Wee! wee!'

Moral
A moral there is to this little song,
  A moral that's easy to see;
Don't try when you're young to say 'Umph! umph!
  umph!'
  For you only can say 'Wee! wee!'

Alfred Scott Gatty

UMPH   UMPH   UMPH   UMPH

A Fish in the Sea

I am a little fish swimming in the sea,
I am a little fish look at me.
Please do not put me on a hook,
And have me for your tea.

John Chalmers
Age 9

Birds on a Stone

There were two birds
Sat on a stone
One flew away
Then there was one
The other flew after
Then there was none
And so the poor stone
Was left all alone.

Anon

I Had a Little Crocodile

I had a little crocodile
I used to call him Fred
And he would walk to school with me
And sleep upon my bed.

We always, always were together
We'd swim and shout and smile
I'm sure you know just what I mean
Had you a crocodile.

What joy to run beneath the stars!
And make a wish, and call it ours!

But best of all we loved to eat!
All cakes and jams and cream
We'd eat at breakfast and at tea
And often in between!

But Fred grew big along with me
And Mum began to say –
'You're too grown-up for just one bed!
So Fred must go away.'

But what my mother really thought
And what she should have said
Was, 'When crocodiles are peckish
They might eat you instead!'

She didn't understand! Oh, Mother!
Do you think friends would eat each other?

I had a little crocodile
Who'd sleep upon my bed
Before we both 'grew-up' too much
I had a friend, called Fred.

Sara Conkey

Horatio Hamilton Harries

Horatio Hamilton Harries,
Loved little Claribel Clarisse
He gave her a taste
For red ju-jube paste;
He said, 'Marry me!'
She replied scornfully,
'At our age nobody marries.'

Anon

Fishy Tale

When fishes set umbrellas up
If the rain-drops run,
Lizards will want their parasols
To shade them from the sun.

When polar bears wear snow-boots
If snow is in the sky
Frogs will want green galoshes
To keep their tootsies dry.

When octopuses wear mittens
On each and every hand
Nightingales will want guitars
To make a new pop band!

Christina Rossetti (verse 1)
Sara Conkey (verses 2 and 3)

Bed in Summer

In winter I get up at night
And dress by yellow candle-light.
In summer, quite the other way,
I have to go to bed by day.

I have to go to bed and see
The birds still hopping on the tree,
Or hear the grown-up people's feet
Still going past me in the street.

And does it not seem hard to you,
When all the sky is clear and blue,
And I should like so much to play,
To have to go to bed by day?

Robert Louis Stevenson

Me and My Dog

Me and my dog went out for a run,
but we stopped. We looked at the clouds.
One of the clouds looked like a moon.
Me and my dog ran on home.

Anna Drodge
Age 5

The Skipping-Rope

Sweet Lilian with the skipping-rope,
You've won my heart from me,
You look so bright, young Lilian:
Says Lilian, 'One, two, three.'

Sweet Lilian with the skipping-rope,
My heart is in a fix,
For I'm in love with someone else:
Cries Lilian, 'Four, five, six.'

Sweet Lilian with the skipping-rope,
Say, will you not be mine?
Don't hit me with your skipping-rope:
Sings Lilian, 'Seven, eight, nine.'

Mrs Charles Heaton

Go to Bed

**Go to bed first –
A golden purse**

**Go to bed second –
A golden pheasant**

**Go to bed third –
A golden bird**

Anon

Water

When I am at home
And in my bed
I think of lots of things
In my head

I think of water
Rushing and curling
I think of waves
Breaking and swirling

I think of the sea
Smooth and calm
And the small waves
That can do no harm

I think of these things
While I lie awake
Just the sea and the waves
As they break

Andrew Thorne
Age 8

The Sad Story of a Little Boy That Cried

Once a little boy, Jack, was, oh! ever so good,
Till he took a strange notion to cry all he could.

So he cried all the day, and he cried all the night,
He cried in the morning, and in the twilight;

He cried till his voice was as hoarse as a crow,
And his mouth grew so large it looked like a great O.

It grew at the bottom, and grew at the top;
It grew till they thought that it never would stop.

Each day his great mouth grew taller and taller,
And his dear little self grew smaller and smaller.

At last, that same mouth grew so big that – alack! –
It was only a mouth with a border of Jack.

Anon

How the Little Kite Learnt to Fly

'I never can do it,' the little kite said,
As he looked at the others high over his head;
I know I should fall if I tried to fly.'
'Try,' said the big kite; 'only try!
Or I fear you never will learn at all.'
But the little kite said, 'I'm afraid I'll fall.'

The big kite nodded: 'Ah, well, good-bye;
I'm off'; and he rose toward the tranquil sky.
Then the little kite's paper stirred at the sight,
And trembling he shook himself free for flight.
First whirling and frightened, then braver grown,
Up, up he rose through the air alone,
Till the big kite looking down could see
The little one rising steadily.

Then how the little kite thrilled with pride,
As he sailed with the big kite side by side!
While far below he could see the ground,
And the boys like small spots moving round.
They rested high in the quiet air,
And only the birds and clouds were there.
'Oh, how happy I am!' the little kite cried;
'And all because I was brave, and tried.'

Anon

The Sea

I like the sea
Because it runs after me
I run up the sand
It follows me
It splashes
Makes all funny noises
Like it is saying
Come with me
I make sand castles
He giggles and knocks them down.

Fiona Sharples
Age 8

An Alphabet of Children

A is for Apt little Annie,
Who lives down in Maine with her grannie.
Such pies she can make!
And such doughnuts and cake!
Oh, we like to make visits to Grannie!

B is for Bad little Bridget,
Who is morn, noon, and night in a fidget.
Her dresses she tears,
And she tumbles down-stairs,
And her mother's most worn to a midget.

These poems were written a long time ago. My Grandad was friends with all these children.

C is for Curious Charlie,
Who lives on rice, oatmeal, and barley.
He once wrote a sonnet
On his mother's best bonnet;
And he lets his hair grow long and snarley.

D is for Dear little Dinah,
Whose manners grow finer and finer.
She smiles and she bows
To the pigs and the cows,
And she calls the old cat Angelina.

E is for Erring young Edward,
Who never can bear to go bedward.
Every evening at eight
He bewails his hard fate,
And they're all quite discouraged with
    Edward.

F is for Foolish Miss Florence,
Who of spiders has such an abhorrence
That she shivers with dread
When she looks overhead,
For she lives where they're plenty – at
    Lawrence.

G is for Glad little Gustave,
Who says that a monkey he *must* have;
But his mother thinks not,
And says that they've got
All the monkey they care for in Gustave.

H is for Horrid young Hannah,
Who has the most shocking bad manner.
Once she went out to dine
With a party of nine,
And she ate every single banana.

I is for Ignorant Ida,
Who doesn't know rhubarb from cider.
Once she drank up a quart,
Which was more than she ought,
And it gave her queer feelings inside her.

J is for Jovial young Jack,
Who goes to the balls in a hack.
He thinks he can dance,
And he'll caper and prance
Till his joints are half ready to crack.

K is for Kind little Katy,
Who weighs 'most a hundred and eighty;
But she eats every day,
And the doctors all say
That's the reason she's growing so weighty.

L is for Lazy young Leicester,
Who works for a grocer in Chester;
But he says he needs rest,
And he finds it is best
To take every day a siesta.

M is for Mournful Miss Molly,
Who likes to be thought melancholy.
She's as limp as a rag
When her sisters play tag.
For it's vulgar, she says, to be jolly.

N is for Naughty young Nat,
Who sat on his father's best hat.
When they asked if he thought
He had done as he ought,
He said he supposed 'twas the cat!

O's Operatic Olivia,
Who visits her aunt in Bolivia.
She can sing to high C –
But, between you and me,
They don't care for that in Bolivia.

P is for Poor little Paul,
Who doesn't like study at all.
But he's learning to speak
In Hebrew and Greek,
And is going to take Sanskrit next fall.

Q is for Queer little Queen,
Who's grown so excessively lean
That she fell in a crack,
And hurt her poor back,
And they say she can hardly be seen.

R is for Rude Master Ruby,
Who once called his sister a booby!
But a boy who stood by
Heard her piteous cry,
And came and chastised Master Ruby.

S is for Stylish young Sadie,
Whose hat is so big and so shady
That she thought it was night
When the sun was out bright,
And mistook an old cow for a lady.

T is for Turbulent Teddy,
Who never can learn to be steady.
He'll skip and he'll hop,
And turn 'round like a top,
And he's broken his leg twice already.

U is Unhappy Ulrica,
Who takes her tea weaker and
    weaker;
She sits in the dust
And eats nothing but crust,
And Moses, they say, wasn't
    meeker.

V is for Valiant young Vivian,
Who practised awhile in obli-
   vion;
Till he saw, without doubt,
He could turn inside out,
And now they're all boasting
   of Vivian.

W is Wise little Willie,
Who lives where the weather
  is chilly;
But he skates and he slides,
And takes lots of sleigh-rides,
And he coasts on his sled where
   it's hilly.

X, Y, Z – each is a baby
Who is going to be wonderful,
   maybe;
For their mothers all say
To themselves every day,
That there never was quite such a baby.

Isabel Frances Bellows

Pob's Alphabet

A is for Andrew
Who fell in the stew

B is for Betty
Who sits on the settee

C is for Carol
Who sleeps in a barrel

D is for Depinder
Who burns toast to a cinder

E is for Eddy
Who rather likes Teddy

F is for Fatima
Whose sister sat on her

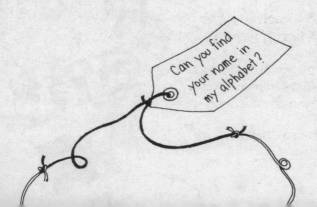

Can you find your name in my alphabet?

How quickly can you say the whole alphabet?

G is for Gertie
Whose knees are all dirty

H is for Hans
Who just likes to dance

I is for Ingrid
Who prefers to eat squid

J is for Jack
Who wears a blue mac

K is for Kamla
Who likes fixing cameras

L is for Lassie
Who's ever so classy

M is for Mike
Who rides a red bike

N is for Nerys
Who sits on the terrace

O is for Omar
Who plays the guitar

P is for Patrick
Who scores lots of hat tricks

Q is for Queenie
Who's ever so weenie

R is for Rishi
Who smells something fishy

My name isn't here but I know it's P for Pob!

How many poems
can you make
using your
friends' names?

S is for Sam
Who does the can-can

T is for Tracy
Who wears frocks that are lacy

U is for Una
Who eats tons of tuna

V is for Vikesh
Who loves to get wet

W is for Wendy
Who's hip and trendy

Y is for Yasmin
Who's not sure where she has been . . .

POB can't think of any more – can you?
POB's sure you can make a rhyme with your name.

Early and Late

Go to bed early – wake up with joy;
Go to bed late – cross girl or boy.
Go to bed early – ready for play;
Go to bed late – moping all day.
Go to bed early – no pains or ills;
Go to bed late – doctors and pills.

W S Reed

From A Song of Myself

There was a naughty boy
    And a naughty boy was he
For nothing would he do
    But scribble poetry –
        He took
        An ink stand
        In his hand
        And a Pen
        Big as ten
        In the other,
        And away
        In a Pother
        He ran
        To the mountains
        And fountains

And ghostes
And Postes
And witches
And ditches
And wrote
In his coat
When the weather
Was cool.
Fear of gout
And without
When the weather
Was warm –
Och the charm
When we choose
To follow one's nose
    To the north,
    To the north,
To follow one's nose
    To the north!

There was a naughty boy,
    And a naughty boy was he,
He ran away to Scotland
    The people for to see –
        Then he found
        That the ground
        Was as hard,
        That a yard
        Was as long
        That a song
        Was as merry,
        That a cherry
        Was as red –
        That lead
        Was as weighty
        That fourscore
        Was as eighty.
        That a door
        Was as wooden
        As in England –
    So he stood in his shoes
        And he wonder'd

He wonder'd

He stood in his shoes

And He wonder'd

John Keats

My Three Cows

I have three fat cows
spoilt to death. Their
names are Susie and Sara and Beth.

One is black and two are red
Beth, the black one,
has a large head.

We feed them with grass
and cake and hay
and they give us a gallon of milk a day.

Sam Clarke
Age 10

A.B.C.

Come hither, little puppy-dog;
I'll give you a new collar
If you will learn to read and spell
And be a clever scholar.
'Oh no,' the little dog replied,
'I've other fish to fry,
For I must learn to guard the house
And bark when thieves are nigh.'

Anon

What Became of Them?

He was a rat, and she was a rat,
And down in one hole they did dwell
And both were as black as a witch's cat,
And they loved one another well.

He had a tail, and she had a tail,
Both long and curling and fine;
And each said, 'Yours is the finest tail
In the world, excepting mine.'

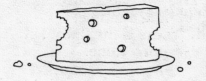

He smelt the cheese, and she smelt the cheese,
And they both pronounced it good;
And both remarked it would greatly add
To the charms of their daily food.

So he ventured out, and she ventured out,
And I saw them go with pain;
But what befell them I never can tell,
For they never came back again.

Anon

Mr Blackbird

Mr Mr Blackbird
how are you,
you see me and I see you,
you come every morning
Waiting to be fed
then you go home at night
to your little bed.

Lynn Maloney
Age 8

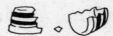

Mrs Mason

Mrs Mason
Broke a basin
Mrs Frost
Asked what it cost
Mrs Brown
Said – 'Half a crown'
Mrs Flory
Said – 'What a story!'

Anon

Long Time Ago

Once there was a little kitty,
    White as the snow;
In a barn she used to frolic
    Long time ago.

In the barn a little mousie
    Ran to and fro,
For she heard the little kitty
    Long time ago.

Two black eyes had little kitty,
    Black as a sloe;
And they spied the little mousie
    Long time ago.

Four soft paws had little kitty,
  Paws soft as snow;
And they caught the little mousie
  Long time ago.

Nine pearl teeth had little kitty,
  All in a row;
And they bit the little mousie
  Long time ago.

When the teeth bit little mousie,
  Mousie cried out, 'Oh!'
But she slipped away from kitty
  Long time ago.

Anon

Pob Says, 'Take Note!'

The coalman's hat is very black,
the baker's hat is whiter.
A sack of coal is hard to lift
but a loaf of bread is lighter.

When spring comes it makes the trees
grow a thousand new green leaves;
but when the autumn turns them brown
then they all come falling down.

If I was big and in the sea
I could be a whale,
but if I'm small and in a shell,
I might just be a snail!

Birds and planes fly in the sky
because of wings they've got
but clouds float without wings at all
so they can't weigh a lot!

In the snowy forest,
the fir tree stood with pride,
but by the frozen river bank,
the weeping willow cried.

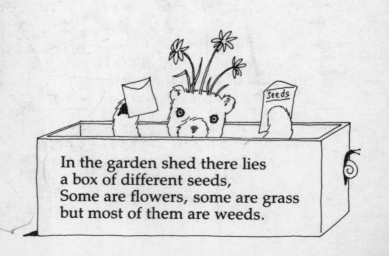

In the garden shed there lies
a box of different seeds,
Some are flowers, some are grass
but most of them are weeds.

Marmalade and butter
are what people spread on toast,
but I like spreading ice cream and
tomato sauce the most.

Apple trees grow apples
and a pear tree grows a pear,
but wintertime the bare trees
never grow a bear.

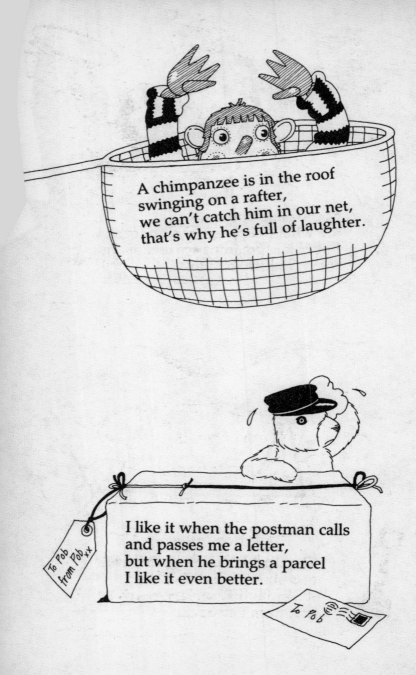

A chimpanzee is in the roof
swinging on a rafter,
we can't catch him in our net,
that's why he's full of laughter.

I like it when the postman calls
and passes me a letter,
but when he brings a parcel
I like it even better.

To Pob
from Pob xx

To Pob

My favourite plate is really great,
it's orange, red and pink,
but the handle off my favourite cup has
got lost down the sink.

The desert is all made of sand
and sunny as can be,
It's rather like a giant beach
that hasn't any sea.

What has three legs and is green
and bigger than a horse
it's got four arms and flies about . . .
a space monster of course.

Granny has a chest of drawers,
in which she keeps her clothes,
she has a big old wardrobe too,
but in that, no one knows!

For Starving Children

Poor starving children you sit there all day.
Your limbs are so weak you can't even play
Poor starving children because of the drought
There is no food to be handed out.
Poor starving children. Help is on the way.
So please try and live for just another day.

Michael Algate
Age 8

Choosing Their Names

Our old cat has kittens three –
What do you think their names should be?

One is tabby with emerald eyes
And a tail long and slender
And in a temper she quickly flies
If you by chance offend her
I think we shall call her this
I think we shall call her that –
Now don't you think that Pepperpot
Is a nice name for a cat?

One is black with a frill of white
And her feet are all white fur
If you stroke her she carries her tail upright
And quickly begins to purr
I think we shall call her this
I think we shall call her that –
Now do you think that Sootikin
Is a nice name for a cat?

One is a tortoise-shell yellow and black
With plenty of white about him
If you tease him at once sets up his back
He's a quarrelsome one, ne'er doubt him
I think we shall call him this
I think we shall call him that –
Now do you think that Scratchaway
Is a nice name for a cat?

Our old cat has kittens three
And I fancy their names will be
Pepperpot, Sootikin and Scratchaway – there!
Were ever kittens with these to compare?
And we call the old mother –
Now what do you think? –
Tabitha Longclaws Tiddley Wink!

Thomas Hood

Three Wise Men of Gotham

Three wise men of Gotham
Went to sea in a bowl:
And if the bowl had been stronger
My song would have been longer.

Traditional

Poems are fun.
Try writing one
about anything you like,
cows, trees, birds or fleas
or your brand new BMX bike.

X Pob